EDDY THE OSTRICH

Liz Freeston

In the depths of South Africa
Amidst the bush and the Big Game,
Lived a handsome small boy
And Vernon was his name.

"Can you get some eggs from the garden?"
His mother asked one day.
So Vernon went to the chicken coop
Then looked amongst the hay.

He found several smallish eggs,
Then he couldn't believe his eyes
For hidden in a dark corner was
An egg twenty times the size.

He carried it back home carefully.
"Look what I've got Mum!" he cried.
"Put it in the dog's bowl," she said
"With straw around the side."

"It needs to go in a warm place," said Mum,
"On the shelf above the heater.
We don't want it eaten or broken now
By your naughty dog called Peter."

Vernon watched the egg every day.
"I'm getting bored with this," he cried
"What's the point of this stupid egg?"
"You must be patient," Mum replied.

One morning Vernon got up earlier
In the dark, an hour before dawn.
He heard a cracking and a crunching;
Eddy the ostrich was finally born.

The egg had cracked right open,
Eddy had a good look around,
He got up with a bit of a wobble
And was about to fall to the ground.

Vernon caught him just in time.
Peter licked his feathers clean.
They wrapped him in a blanket,
The biggest chick they'd ever seen.

"This is no ordinary chick," said Mum,
"Double kneecaps and a very long neck.
Only two toes he has on each foot,
It's an ostrich with a very hard peck!"

Eddy grew bigger day by day.
He watched smaller birds up in the trees.
"I must exercise myself in the garden," he said
"So that I can fly as well as these."

He'd run down the length of the garden,
As fast as he could possibly race,
Then jump up in the air
And fall flat upon his face.

Eddy was getting fed up with this
And then he began to cry.
"What's the point of me being a bird
When I can't even learn to fly?"

"Don't worry, my dear," said Mum.
"There are lots of things you can do.
You are a very fast runner, you know.
You have lovely black feathers too!"

"I'll give Vernon a ride to school," said Eddy
"It will save him from taking the bus.
We will overtake the other children
No one will be quicker than us!"

So this happened on a regular basis.
Peter followed but a long way behind.
They'd wait outside 'til school was over.
None of the teachers seemed to mind.

The school friends wanted to ride Eddy.
It was all they wanted to do.
So Eddy was kind and cooperative
And let them have a ride too.

One day, when Eddy was at home on his own
He thought, "My toenails need to be shorter."
He scratched them against the tables and chairs
And did more damage than he did ought "ter".

Next morning, Mum shouted, with a very cross face,
"Eddy, come here now, don't you hide.
Look at the damage you've done in my house,
You must live on your own outside!"

Eddy went out with tears in his eyes.
"What a naughty ostrich I've been!
Perhaps Mum will like me a little bit better
If I give the house a clean."

"Can I come inside to dust the house?" asked Eddy.
"Well, just this once," Mum did respond.
So he dusted the house with his big black feathers
Then went outside to wash in the pond.

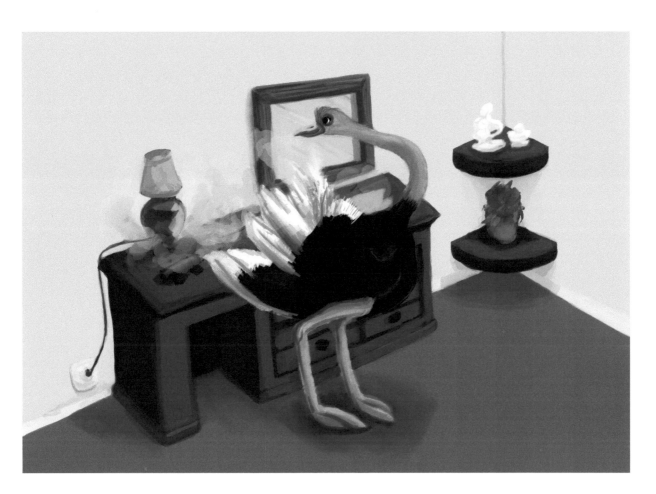

11

Mum said, "I like you a little better now,
But outside you must always stay."
Peter and Vernon ran out to join him;
They had fun for the rest of the day.

Next day, Eddy and his friends got up early.
"Let's go to the town for a change," they said.
They saw a sign for a horserace later that day
'Five thousand rand for the winner' it read.

"Eddy, you're a fast runner," Vernon cried,
"Let's see if you can possibly enter."
"But I'm only an ostrich," Eddy replied
"I don't know if I'm really meant "ter"."

"Can Eddy enter the race?" asked Vernon.
"We know he's not a horse.
I can be his jockey," he said
"We'd like to run this course!"

The man laughed – "Have a bird in the race?
Now let me show you the door."
"I'm not totally a bird," cried Eddy
"I'm descended from the dinosaur!"

The man said, "Well, if you must, you must.
You can wear running vest number nine.
Come on now, and hurry along,
Get yourself to the starting line."

So Eddie lined up with all of the rest.
The flag was lowered to start the race.
Eddy's toe got stuck in some blades of grass.
The horses began at a terrific pace.

"Wait for me," cried Eddy. "Let me catch you up.
Remember I'm really only a beginner."
He overtook all the other runners,
He was fastest and became the winner.

The prize-giving was a great celebration,
Musicians and a big brass band.
Eddy had a great big smile on his face.
He won a trophy and five thousand rand.

Eddy, Vernon and Peter rushed home.
Eddy cried, "Mum, look what I've just won!
I can pay for new tables and chairs for the house
And make up for the damage I've done."

Mum said "What a wonderful bird you are!
I'm sorry I made all that fuss.
You won't have to live outside anymore,
You can live in the house with us."

Next morning, Eddy got up bright and early.
He left Peter and Vernon behind.
Then he ran to the local recycling centre
To see what he could find.

He found some wood, a cart and some goggles,
An engine and an old pair of skis.
He paid for these at the recycling shop.
"I'm going to make something great with these!"

He placed everything into the cart with care.
"I've a great idea!" thought Ed.
He rushed home as fast as he could,
Then locked himself in the shed.

Three days later, Eddy came out at last.
He said, "For once, I've used my brain.
With the bits I bought from the recycling shop
I've built myself a plane."

So Eddy showed the others what he'd done.
He climbed into the pilot's seat.
His legs went through holes in the bottom.
"I will take off using my feet!"

Eddy asked Vernon and Peter to help him
Push the plane into the nearby lane.
Then he carefully put on his goggles
And sat in the pilot's seat again.

"Wish me luck!" Eddy cried to his friends,
Then turned the ignition to start the propeller.
"I must run as fast as I can now,
I'm really a fit little "feller"".

His feet started moving slowly at first,
But his legs had plenty of power.
He managed to run much faster,
Then took off at sixty miles per hour.

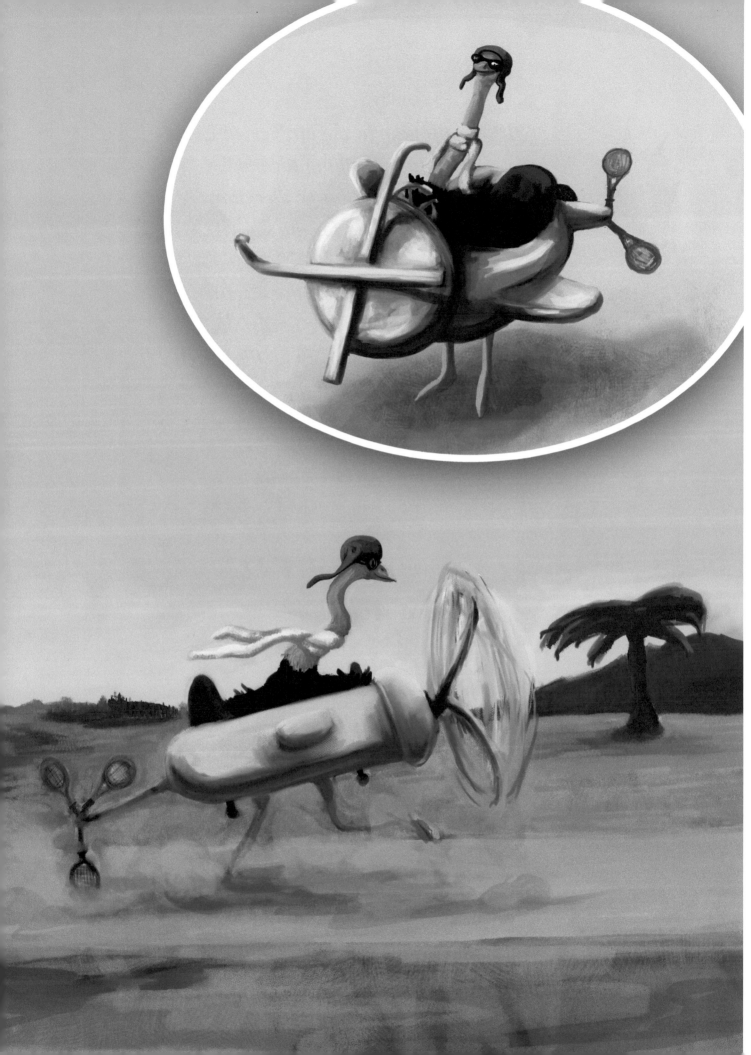

"It's exciting up in the air," cried Eddy,
"It's just the thing for me."
He started to change direction
And headed for the sea.

He saw Cape Town in the distance.
"There is something I must do."
He made the plane fly up higher,
Over Table Mountain he flew.

"One of the wonders of nature," thought Eddy
"But now the journey ends.
I'm feeling very hungry now
I must get back to my friends."

He headed back home quickly.
In the distance were Vernon and Pete.
He brought the plane down carefully
And landed on his feet.

Vernon and Peter were cheering.
Mum rushed into the lane.
"It was magic!" cried Eddy excitedly,
"I can't wait to do it again!"

"That was the best day of my life!" cried Eddy,
As a tear fell from his eye.
"I know the point of me being here now,
I'M AN OSTRICH, A BIRD, AND I CAN FLY!"

THE END

ABOUT THE AUTHOR

Liz Freeston, the author, has been a teacher and examiner of English as a Foreign Language for many years. She is currently a Chief Examiner for a well-known examination board in the UK.

The inspiration for this book has come from Liz's fascination with ostriches, following several visits to various ostrich farms in South Africa over the past few years. She has included some interesting facts about these characterful birds in this fun children's book.

Copyright © 2020 by Elizabeth Anne Freeston

First paperback edition October 2020

Illustrations by Ciara E. White
Book design by Publishing Push

ISBN Paperback: 978-1-913704-77-3
ISBN eBook: 978-1-913704-78-0

CPSIA information can be obtained
at www.ICGtesting.com
Printed in the USA
BVHW022100260822
645602BV00002B/93